Trouble with Mr. Tremblay

by
ROBERT DOUGLAS

Beacon Hill Press of Kansas City
Kansas City, Missouri

Copyright 2002
by Beacon Hill Press of Kansas City

Printed in the United States of America

ISBN 083-411-9358

Cover Design: Sharon Page
Cover Illustrator: Keith Alexander
Inside Illustrations: Keith Alexander

Editor: Donna Manning
Associate Editor: Kathleen M. Johnson

Note: This fictional book is part of the *Understanding
Christian Mission,* Children's Mission Education curricu-
lum. It is designed for use in Year 2, The Bible and Mission. Lessons focus on the Bible and how it helps mis-
sionaries tell others about God's love.

10   9   8   7   6   5   4   3   2   1

Dedicated to Ian, Sarah,
Brittany, Jon, and Colin

Contents

1. Too Young   7

2. A Plan   10

3. The Accident   14

4. A New Friend   17

5. An Unexpected Visitor   22

6. Another Surprise   27

7. A New School   31

1

Too Young

"Mom!" Jamie said in a loud whisper. "I can raise $5,000. I can!"

"Shhh. Don't be silly," his mother whispered. "The missionary didn't ask you to raise money. You're too young."

"I'm nine years old," he thought to himself. "I want to help."

Jamie always wanted to help. And he wanted to learn how Jesus helped others. He never missed an opportunity to be in church. He didn't want to miss a church service, his Sunday School class, and especially Vacation Bible School.

But Jamie wanted to do more to serve Jesus. Jamie felt called by God to be a missionary.

Jamie listened with special interest this Sunday morning because there was a missionary speaker. He wanted to hear the missionary's exciting stories about what God was doing in Peru.

"The church is praying that I'll raise the $5,000 while I'm here in Canada," said the missionary. "We want to help the Quechua [KE-chuh-wuh] Indians in our village. We want to build a cinder-block mission school for their children."

"There must be a way I can help the missionary raise money to build a school," thought Jamie.

The missionary sang a few Quechuan songs and recited John 3:16 in the Quechuan language.

Even though Jamie did not understand the words, he knew John 3:16 was true. "Everyone needs Jesus," said Jamie softly.

Suddenly, Jamie had an idea.

2

A Plan

"I've got it!" shouted Jamie. All the way home from church Jamie had thought about the stories the missionary told. The more he thought about his idea, the more excited he became.

"Mom, Dad!" Jamie hurried to the table for dinner. His father prayed the blessing. Jamie couldn't wait any longer. "I have a plan!" he blurted out. "I'll collect all the empty cans and bottles I can find. Then I'll take them to the recycle center. I will give the money I earn to the missionary."

"Jamie, do you know how many bottles and cans you would have to collect to raise $5,000?" his mother asked.

"No, I don't know," Jamie answered honestly. "If I get 10 cents for every . . ."

"Fifty thousand!" she interrupted.

"Wow! I guess you better get started," chuckled his father as he winked at Jamie. Jamie winked back.

"But, Jamie," said his mother, "you should enjoy your summer vacation."

"I will," Jamie said. "Collecting bottles and cans will be lots of fun. I know God wants me to help the children in Peru."

"Obeying God is important," said his father.

"That's true," Mother agreed. "You should obey God."

"I'll help you get the bottles and cans to the recycle center," offered his father.

"Thanks!" exclaimed Jamie.

"And I'll get dessert." Mother went into the kitchen and returned a moment later with their favorite dessert—hot apple pie. "Surprise!" she said with a big smile.

"Yea!" Jamie cheered. "I love surprises, especially a surprise like apple pie!"

His mother cut each of them a big slice. Then she topped it with a scoop of vanilla ice cream. They all agreed it was the best pie she had ever made.

The next morning, Jamie tied his red wagon to the back of his bike. He began searching for empty bottles and cans. Jamie's first stop was the ball field, where he found mostly cans.

But by the end of the day, he had quite a collection of empty cans and bottles.

Jamie's father helped him put them in a bag. Then they took them to the recycle center. They gave their bag to the teenage boy behind the counter. Jamie could hardly wait for the boy to count all of the bottles and cans.

"Dad, do you think my collection is worth $100?"

"I don't know. You've worked hard."

The boy finished counting and looked up at Jamie. "I owe you $10.00," he said.

"Ten dollars!" exclaimed Jamie. "That's all? It will take me *forever* to raise enough money for the mission school! Maybe I am too young."

"Jamie, I'm proud of your effort. You have a good plan." Jamie's father encouraged him.

Jamie decided to try again. The next day he looked everywhere he could think of for more bottles and cans. That's when it happened!

3

The Accident

"What have you done?" shouted Mr. Tremblay (trahm-BLAY) as he ran out his front door. "Look at my flowers! You have destroyed my prize chrysanthemums!"

Jamie just sat in the mud. He could not believe it. "Both of my knees are skinned. The front wheel of my bike is bent. And all he can think about is his flowers!" mumbled Jamie to himself.

"Look at all this broken glass!" the man continued yelling. "Pick up your things, and get out of here!"

Jamie picked himself up out of the wet dirt and tried to explain what happened. He told Mr. Tremblay that it was the hole in the sidewalk that sent him flying over the handlebars and into the middle of his flower bed. But Mr. Tremblay was not listening to Jamie. He was sweeping up the broken glass and still complaining about his ruined flowers.

Jamie picked up the cans and bottles that were not broken. He put them in the wagon, which was still tied to the back of his bike. Then he slowly pushed his bike out of Mr. Tremblay's yard.

When Jamie got home, his mother cleaned

and bandaged both of his knees. She tried to comfort him. "I don't want you to collect any more bottles or cans today," she said.

That night Jamie talked with his parents about what happened in Mr. Tremblay's flower bed.

"He didn't care about me," Jamie complained. "All he cared about was his flowers."

"They must be very important to him," said Father.

"So what," answered Jamie. "No wonder everyone thinks he's mean."

"Do you think that's OK?" asked Mother. "Is that what Jesus would want?"

"No," answered Jamie.

At bedtime he prayed for Mr. Tremblay and asked God to bless him.

4

A New Friend

The next morning Jamie made an important decision.

"I know what Jesus wants me to do," he told his mother. "I have $10 from collecting cans and bottles, and $8 from Grandmother for my birthday. That should be enough."

"Enough for what?" asked Mother.

Jamie told his mother about his decision.

"I'll pray for you, Jamie."

Jamie took his wagon to the Lawn and Garden Shop a few blocks from home. He bought three trays of flowers for $15, plus tax. He loaded them into his wagon and walked to Mr. Tremblay's house.

Jamie whispered a prayer as he knocked on the front door. When Mr. Tremblay opened the door, Jamie began to explain. "I've come to replace the flowers I ruined."

"Just go away and leave me alone," Mr. Tremblay told him.

"Please, Sir, I spent all my money to buy these flowers. I was saving the money to help our missionary build a school for children in Peru. And besides," he looked up at Mr. Tremblay, "the lady at the Lawn and Garden Shop told me I couldn't return them."

Mr. Tremblay looked down at the collection of petunias, pansies, and marigolds in Jamie's wagon. His voice softened. "They're not mums. But I guess they'll do," he said with a smile. "Wait here a moment." He went into the house to get a spade.

"Here," he said when he returned, "you can dig with this small shovel."

"Thank you," Jamie said with a smile. He pulled his wagon to the edge of the flower bed. He began removing the flowers he had ruined the day before.

In a short time, Jamie had all of the old flowers removed and two trays of new flowers planted. He was almost finished when he saw Mr. Tremblay on the porch. He was carrying a tray with a pitcher and two glasses.

"Would you like some lemonade?" he called.

"Yes!" Jamie exclaimed. "I'd love some-

thing cold to drink." He joined Mr. Tremblay on the porch steps. "It sure is hot today."

"Yes, it is," agreed Mr. Tremblay as he handed Jamie a tall glass of lemonade. "Earlier you said something about saving your money to help build a school. Tell me about the school."

"Oh, it's a mission school." Jamie's face lit up. "A missionary from Peru visited our church. She told us about the Quechua Indian children in her village. The missionary said it would cost $5,000 to build a small school for them. I plan to help raise the money. The children need a school where they can learn about Jesus."

"So why did you spend your savings to buy these flowers for me?" asked Mr. Tremblay.

"Well, at first I was angry at you. But then I asked myself, 'What would Jesus want me to do?' I knew the answer. God loves you, and He wants me to love you too. That's why I bought the flowers."

"Why would God love a mean, old man like me?" Mr. Tremblay asked.

"God loves everyone," answered Jamie. "He wants us to share His love with others. God sent His Son, Jesus, to die on a cross so our sins could be forgiven. If we ask Him to forgive our sins, He will. Then we can have God's love in our hearts."

"I want that kind of love," said Mr. Tremblay. "Thank you for doing what Jesus asked you to do."

Mr. Tremblay held out his hand. "By the way, I'm Mr. Tremblay."

"I know," said Jamie. "I'm Jamie Arnold."

"It's nice to meet such a fine young man," said Mr. Tremblay.

"Likewise," said Jamie as they shook hands.

"Well, I better get back to work," Jamie said.

"May I help you?" asked Mr. Tremblay.

"Of course," answered Jamie with a grin.

The two worked together and finished the job in no time.

"It looks very nice," admitted Mr. Tremblay.

5

An Unexpected Visitor

"I'm so glad you came!" exclaimed Jamie as he ran to greet Mr. Tremblay.

"Me too," he replied.

Jamie was surprised to see Mr. Tremblay at their Wednesday night prayer meeting. But he was more surprised when Mr. Tremblay stood up to talk.

"This week a young boy almost destroyed my flower bed. However, he spent his entire savings to replace the damaged flowers. He said it's what Jesus wanted him to do."

Mr. Tremblay looked at Jamie and continued. "Jamie Arnold said that God loves me and would forgive my sins if I asked Him. I did ask Him. Now I have God's love in my heart too."

Everyone thanked God that Mr. Tremblay asked Jesus into his heart. They sang songs and then closed the service with prayer.

Jamie and Mr. Tremblay became good friends. Mr. Tremblay helped Jamie collect bottles and cans almost every day. They often had picnics together.

If it rained, they sat in Mr. Tremblay's living room and listened to music. Sometimes Mr. Tremblay read out loud from one of the many old, leather-bound books in his library. Jamie

thought the sea adventures were the most exciting.

The change in Mr. Tremblay's life was clear to everyone who knew him. People wondered what caused him to change. Mr. Tremblay told them about his new life in Christ and how they could ask Jesus into their hearts.

While Jamie and Mr. Tremblay collected cans and bottles, they talked about many things. Jamie told Mr. Tremblay that God had called him to become a missionary. Mr. Tremblay told Jamie how he used to pilot a ferry across the Northumberland Strait between Nova Scotia and Prince Edward Island. That sounded exciting to Jamie, but not as exciting as being a missionary.

By the end of the summer, Jamie and his new friend had collected almost $350 worth of cans and bottles. It was not the $5,000 Jamie had hoped to collect. Still, it was a lot of money.

On the last Sunday of summer vacation, Mr. Arnold arranged for Jamie and Mr. Tremblay to present the money to Pastor Davis. But when they were called forward, only Jamie walked onto the platform. Mr. Tremblay was not there.

The pastor thanked Jamie for all of his hard work on the project. He called Jamie's parents forward to thank them for their help. Jamie was very excited but wondered what had happened to Mr. Tremblay.

6

Another Surprise

After church Jamie ran to Mr. Tremblay's house. "How could he forget such an important Sunday?" Jamie wondered. He could hardly wait to tell Mr. Tremblay about the morning service. When he arrived, a young man who looked like Mr. Tremblay was locking the front door.

"I'm looking for Mr. Tremblay," Jamie said catching his breath.

"I'm Mr. Tremblay," replied the young man.

"I mean the Mr. Tremblay who lives here," Jamie said.

"Are you Jamie?" he asked.

"Yes, I am," Jamie answered.

The man looked sad. "My father was expecting you today. Have a seat." Jamie sat down on the porch steps. The young Mr. Tremblay sat down next to him.

"When we visited my father a few weeks ago, he told us about you. He said you helped him find a new life in Christ. We were very excited!"

"Me too," said Jamie.

"But last night, I got a phone call from my father. He asked me to come over right away because he was not feeling well. By the time I got here, he was feeling worse. So I took him to the hospital. On the way he gave me this envelope for you."

"Can we go and see him?" Jamie asked.

"I'm afraid not, Jamie. You see, he passed away very early this morning."

Jamie put his head in his hands. This was worse than skinned knees and a broken bike. He lost a good friend.

Young Mr. Tremblay put his arm around Jamie's shoulder. "Thank you for sharing God's love with my father."

Jamie slowly walked home with the envelope in his hand. He did not want to open it. Tears stung his eyes as he told his mother about Mr. Tremblay.

"Mom, will you read Mr. Tremblay's letter to me?" he asked.

"Of course." She opened the envelope. "Jamie, I think you'll want to read this yourself," she said. She gave him the handwritten note.

"Dear Jamie," it began. "Thank you for helping me. I could never repay you. Enclosed is a check. I think you'll know what to do with it. Sincerely, Albert Tremblay."

Jamie looked into the envelope and found a check for $10,000. "Yes, I do know what to do with it!" he exclaimed.

7

A New School

Jamie stood with his parents in front of the new cinder-block school in Peru. Beside the front door was a small brass plate that read, "In memory of Albert M. Tremblay. He came to know Jesus through the love of one boy."

The Quechuan people sang songs in a language Jamie did not understand. But he knew they were praising God for the school. Jamie felt right at home.

Jamie spoke a few words in Mr. Tremblay's place. The missionary translated Jamie's words to help the Quechuan people understand what he said.

Jamie told the people about his plan to help the missionary raise money. He told them about the bike accident and how Mr. Tremblay had come to know Jesus. He couldn't hold back the tears as he told how Mr. Tremblay helped him with his plan to raise money for the mission school.

Everyone learned something that morning. They learned the importance of sharing God's love. They learned God is faithful to supply our needs. And they learned that God can use young people to accomplish His plans.